GREAT BIBLE STORIES

SAMSON AND DELILAH

Adapted by Maxine Nodel   **Illustrated by Norman Nodel**

BARONET BOOKS is a registered trademark of Playmore Inc., Publishers
and Waldman Publishing Corp., New York, N.Y.

BARONET BOOKS, NEW YORK, NEW YORK
Printed in China

When the Philistines ruled in the land of Israel, there lived a man and wife who had no children. One day, an angel came to the woman and told her she would have a son. And, said the angel, that son would be a Nazarite.

A Nazarite was one who made a promise that, for a certain period of time, he would devote himself to God. During that time, a Nazarite would neither cut his hair nor drink any kind of wine.

The child was born, and named Samson. He grew up, not only a Nazarite, but one of the strongest men in all of Israel. Once a lion attacked him. Samson killed the beast with only his bare hands.

But Samson fell in love with a girl of the Philistines. Against his parents' wishes, he went to a town called Timnah to marry her.

On the way, Samson passed the place where he had killed the lion. A swarm of honeybees were in the lion's skin and Samson took some of the honey to nourish himself as he went.

The wedding at Timnah lasted a whole week. Samson put a riddle to thirty of the young male guests. "If you can answer the riddle in seven days, I will give each man fine linen clothes. If no one can answer, then each must give me such clothes."

The young men agreed.

"This then is the riddle," said Samson. "Out of the eater came forth something to eat. Out of the strong came something sweet."

The answer was the honey in the lion-skin, but no one guessed it. The men asked Samson's wife for help. She begged Samson to tell her, and when he did, she told the men.

On the last day, the men faced Samson. "It was the honey in the skin of the lion you killed."

Samson was very angry. He left his wife and returned to his father's house.

Later, when his anger lessened, Samson went back for his wife. But her father would not let Samson see her. Samson was furious. He burned down all the cornfields of the Philistines.

When the Philistines learned this, they burned the house of Samson's father-in-law, killing the old man and Samson's wife.

The evil went on and on. Samson killed many of the wicked Philistines, until he had to flee far away and live in a cave.

Samson caused so much trouble that the fearful men of Judah came to the cave to hand him over to their Philistine lords.

"I only did to them as they had done to me," Samson told the men. But they tied him with ropes and led him away.

But God's power was still with Samson. He broke his ropes and, with the jawbone of an ass as his only weapon, he destroyed many of the Philistines. Then he escaped to Gaza.

There, the people again tried to capture him. They waited until morning to seize him.

But Samson stayed there only until midnight. He left, taking the very gates of the city with him.

Later, Samson fell in love with Delilah, another Philistine woman. The Philistines used her to capture Samson.

"Find out what makes this Israelite so strong and we will pay you well," they said.

Delilah worked hard to get Samson to tell her the secret of his strength. But he would not reveal the truth.

"You do not love me, or you would tell me," she challenged him.

She kept after him until Samson gave in.
"I am a Nazarite. I am dedicated to God. My hair has never been cut and there lies my strength. If it is cut, I will be as weak as any other man."

Delilah told the Philistines she had learned Samson's secret. They gave her the money they had promised her.

That night, as Samson slept, Delilah brought in a man to cut Samson's hair. She told Samson that he had lost his strength, but he didn't believe her.

When he felt his hair, Samson knew it was true. The Philistines came for him, blinding him and forcing him to work like a beast in their grinding mill.

But God was with Samson, and his hair began to grow.

The Philistines worshipped a cruel idol called Dagon. They held a great festival to honor Dagon and brought Samson, blind and tied, to their temple.

Samson was placed between the giant pillars that supported the temple. The crowds of Philistines mocked and tormented him. He suffered greatly, but he didn't forget his dedication to God.

He prayed for strength to crush the idol-worshipping Philistines. He knew that he too would die. But Samson was ready to sacrifice himself for his God and his people.

Samson put his mighty arms around the pillars and pushed with all his strength. The temple came crashing down on the Philistines and on Samson, crushing them all.

The Philistines were destroyed. Israel was free.